This is a fictionalised biography describing some of the key moments (so far!) in the career of Serge Gnabry.
Some of the events described in this book are based upon the author's imagination and are probably not entirely accurate representations of what actually happened.

Tales from the Pitch
Serge Gnabry
by Harry Coninx

Published by Raven Books
An imprint of Ransom Publishing Ltd.
Unit 7, Brocklands Farm, West Meon, Hampshire GU32 1JN, UK
www.ransom.co.uk

ISBN   978 178591 977 0
First published in 2020
Reprinted 2021 (three times)

There is a reading comprehension quiz available for this book in the popular
Accelerated Reader® software system. For information about ATOS, Accelerated
Reader, quiz points and reading levels please visit www.renaissance.com. Accelerated
Reader, AR, the Accelerated Reader Logo, and ATOS are trademarks of Renaissance
Learning, Inc. and its subsidiaries, registered common law or applied for in the U.S.
and other countries. Used under license.

TALES FROM THE PITCH

SERGE GNABRY

HARRY CONINX

RAVEN

For my best friend, Merv.
A reminder of what Arsenal could have had …

CONTENTS

I

BE AFRAID

October 2019, Tottenham Hotspur Stadium, London, England
Champions League, Bayern Munich v Tottenham Hotspur

"Nervous, Serge?" Joshua Kimmich whispered.

Serge glanced around to see a big grin on his old friend's face.

"I'm fine," he replied firmly.

"Wait until the booing starts," Robert Lewandowski, further back in the tunnel, quickly chimed in.

Serge just rolled his eyes. He half-wished he hadn't

shared his concerns, as an ex-Arsenal player, about playing in front of Tottenham's fans.

But suddenly his Bayern Munich team-mates had to stop their teasing, as a member of Spurs's backroom staff was signalling for them to move.

Minutes later, the players were walking out on to the pitch.

Even at the group stages Champions League nights always brought a special feeling, and the atmosphere in Tottenham's new stadium took Serge's breath away.

With the crisp autumn evening already dark, floodlights lit the pitch dramatically and the roaring of the fans was building in the surrounding shadows. It was a scene asking for a spectacle – and Bayern were in a rush to provide it.

With less than a minute on the clock, Serge found himself collecting the ball in the middle of the pitch – with plenty of space ahead of him.

He used his pace to get himself clear of the defenders and into the box, but then he saw Spurs centre-back Toby Alderweireld bearing down on him. In a flash of panic, he fired the ball straight down Hugo Lloris's throat.

"Come on, man!" he shouted, frustrated by the fact that he'd let the pressure of the occasion get to him.

He was punished for his mistake barely 10 minutes later. A slip-up at the back gifted the ball to Spurs striker Heung-Min Son, who ruthlessly smashed it past Manuel Neuer to put Spurs one up.

As Serge trudged back into the Bayern half for the restart, he avoided his team-mates' eyes. Everybody in the stadium knew that the winner of this game would top this Champions League group – and would therefore get the easier second-round tie.

It was Joshua Kimmich who dragged Bayern back into the game. He picked the ball up about 25 yards out, flicked it onto his right foot and then fired it straight at the Spurs goal.

Serge raised his arms high in the air as he watched it ripple the back of the net. Bayern were back level.

But for the next 20 minutes Spurs were dominant and Bayern had to weather a storm of pressure.

"How is it still 1-1?" Serge heard his fellow winger Kingsley Coman say to Jérôme Boateng, as Tottenham missed yet another chance.

It wasn't until the 44th minute that Bayern were able to create another chance of their own. The ball was bobbling around in the box, with neither Serge or Kingsley quite able to get it under control.

"Rob! Coming your way!" Serge shouted, deciding to spin it towards Bayern's prolific striker. Efficient as ever, Robert Lewandowski fired it into the bottom corner of the goal.

Out of nothing, and completely against the run of play, Bayern had taken the lead.

"What would we do without you?" Serge shouted in Robert's ear as they walked off the pitch at half-time.

It was soon clear, however, that Bayern manager Niko Kovač was less than impressed with their performance, despite the fact they were in front.

"It was casual and it was complacent. That's not us – we're Bayern Munich. And you," he said, looking around the dressing room, "are Bayern Munich players. Now, go and do what Bayern players do."

Serge felt goosebumps rising on his arms.

On this, his first return to north London since joining the Bundesliga, Serge had wanted to show everyone what he could do – how the German league had honed his skills.

So far in this game, he'd missed a chance and had helped set something up for Robert. He needed to do better.

He glanced around at his team-mates. He'd worked hard to be able to play in a side littered with superstars, and he needed to prove that this was where he belonged.

A few minutes into the second half, he'd already stepped it up, bursting away down the left and accelerating away from the Tottenham defenders.

His electrifying pace got him into the box and, just as before, he caught sight of a Spurs defender running at him. But this time he felt no flash of panic. He just picked his spot in the far corner and fired the ball into it.

GOAL!

Serge jogged towards the crowd, celebrating the inch-perfect goal in the same way he always did – pretending to hold a spoon in one hand and a bowl in the other, stirring the air.

"What would we do without *you*?" Robert shouted as the team leapt on him, but Serge wasn't listening.

Deep down, he felt that he hadn't finished stirring things up yet.

As soon as play resumed, he got another. A mistake from Harry Winks let Bayern's Corentin Tolisso in, and he slipped the ball to Serge, who was already making a run into the box.

The ball fell to Serge's left foot and he sent it flying into the corner.

GOAL!

Niko was punching the air on the touchline, the Bayern fans were on their feet, and the Tottenham defenders looked bewildered.

That was his second goal in three minutes. Bayern were running rampant.

Harry Kane handed Spurs a life-line by sneaking a penalty past Neuer to make it 4-2, but it wasn't enough.

With 10 minutes left, Serge burst through once more, opening up space between himself and the defenders. He knew they weren't going to catch him – nobody could *ever* catch him.

Hugo Lloris came rushing out to close it down, but it

was too late – Serge neatly put the ball in the corner of the net.

GOAL!

"A hat-trick!" Coutinho bellowed. "I bet Arsenal are loving you now!"

A couple of minutes later Robert got himself on the scoresheet again, poking the ball into the back of the net after a slick Bayern move. Now Bayern had six.

As the Polish striker stood in front of the fans, arms wide, Serge caught his eye – and Robert raised his eyebrows in return.

Was he daring him to push it even further?

It was a challenge Serge welcomed, and in the 88th minute he proved, for the fourth time that night, just how deadly he was.

He picked the ball up just inside the box and fizzed it directly at goal, straight down the middle.

He hit it with such power that Hugo Lloris could do nothing to stop it.

GOAL!

Serge could hear boos from some of the home crowd, but he needn't have feared – the dissatisfaction wasn't

13

being directed at him. Rather, it was for the Tottenham defence. For the first time in a major competition, Spurs had conceded seven goals at home.

Two minutes later, when the final whistle blew, Serge had to take a moment to appreciate that Bayern hadn't *just* beaten last season's Champions League runners-up – they had humiliated them.

With four of those goals having his name on them, he'd been central to a result that would send shockwaves around Europe.

By the time Niko had come rushing over to him, Kingsley was pretending to slap his cheek, to let him know he wasn't dreaming.

"What a performance!" the manager roared, before turning to the the rest of the team. "We've sent a message to the rest of Europe tonight, lads. They need to be afraid of Bayern Munich!"

He paused, throwing his head back and lifting his arms into the air, "and they need to be absolutely terrified of Serge Gnabrryyy!"

2
STUTTGART'S SPRINTER

July 2005, Serge's primary school, Stuttgart, Germany

"Ready ... "

Ten-year-old Serge crouched down, putting one knee on the ground and his hands out in front of him.

"Set ... "

Straightening his legs, backside in the air, he took a deep breath and listened for the final word.

"GO!"

He was off like a shot, pumping his arms up and down and lifting his knees high. It was only a matter of seconds before he was hurtling across the finish line.

By the time the rest of his classmates had joined him, he was already standing still, bent over double with his hands on his knees.

"Well, you beat everyone easily again, but that wasn't your best 100 metres."

Serge looked up to the see the PE teacher who ran his school's Saturday Athletics Club standing over him, holding his stopwatch.

"No way," Serge replied indignantly, "honest, sir, that was my best effort."

"Come on, Serge," his teacher said, giving him a doubting look, "be honest with me. I don't mind. I just want to understand why you don't seem to be improving any more."

Out of the corner of his eye, Serge noticed his dad's car pulling up across the sport field.

"I just find it difficult," Serge said, distractedly. "When I play football there's something to run after, something to chase. But here there's nothing … it's just *running*."

His teacher smiled. It was no secret that football was really Serge's sport – and everybody knew that he was very good at it.

"Your dad told me you need to leave a bit early today, to go to that tournament across town. So don't worry, I won't keep you. We can work on this next week."

His teacher paused. "But don't give up on sprinting yet, Serge. You could represent our state one day – and even the Olympics isn't out of the question, with talent like yours."

Serge grinned and gave his teacher a little nod, before rushing straight over to his dad and piling into the back of his car.

"Woah! You excited then?" Jean-Hermann Gnabry asked, though the answer was obvious.

The annual youth tournament was something that Serge looked forward to every year. This year, his dad had promised his son lifts to and from the tournament, as well as a new pair of football boots.

Last month, Serge had been offered a place at Bayern Munich's football academy, but Jean-Hermann had decided that Serge was still too young to move so far away from home.

It had been the right decision. Serge had an attacking mindset that made him fantastic on the pitch, but he tended to get overexcited and sometimes needed calming down.

Serge, of course, had been furious at the time – so angry that he'd not spoken to his dad for a whole week – but Jean-Hermann had known that his son would come around eventually. The pair were, after all, extremely close.

"The team who wins it has to attack from the off … you know, put their opponents on the back foot," Serge babbled confidently from the back seat. "Three in the first 10 minutes should do it."

"That's one way, Serge," Jean-Hermann replied, "but keeping a clean sheet by being solid at the back is important as well."

They continued to talk football until they pulled up at the sports ground where the tournament was being hosted.

Serge immediately jumped out of the car and started looking around excitedly. In every corner of the ground squads were warming up, coaches were giving

18

last-minute team talks and refs were chatting in little groups.

He was already caught up in the electrifying atmosphere.

Serge spent the day eagerly dragging his dad around the pitches, trying to see all the best games.

But none of the games came close to the U18s final, right at the end of the day. Serge watched the match wide-eyed, but he quickly became obsessed with one player who clearly outclassed everybody else on the pitch.

This teenager's passes were crisp, his dribbling was mesmerising and each of his crosses found its target with eerie precision.

"He's got to be the best player I've ever seen, Dad," Serge gushed.

Jean-Hermann nodded in agreement. "His name's Mesut Özil. I was talking to some of the other parents and it seems he's become a bit of a celebrity at tournaments like this."

At the end of the match Serge queued up alongside a small group of other boys to say hello to this football prodigy.

"I wish I had someone on my team who played passes like that – I'd score so many goals," he babbled.

"I'm sure you would," Mesut laughed, posing for a quick picture with him.

Mesut's four words were enough to keep Serge talking non-stop all the way home, and by the time they finished their journey he'd made an important decision.

Next year, he didn't want to be watching that tournament. He wanted to be *playing* in it, entertaining the crowds with dazzling displays of football – just like his new hero.

3
ON TO THE NEXT ONE

July 2006, Stuttgart sports ground, Stuttgart

"So if we don't win this game, will you be off to the next club round the corner?" Serge's friend Max asked, as they warmed up before the game.

Serge laughed. He knew he had a reputation for moving clubs often, but he didn't care. After all, it had got him here – playing for Stuttgarter Kickers, in the tournament that last year he'd only been able to watch.

Once he'd realised that his previous team, Feuerbach, were never going to qualify for a tournament place, his dad had helped him find a better club.

"There's no harm in trying out different things," Jean-Hermann had said. "That's how you learn."

"Well, Stuttgarter Kickers are a big team," Max reminded him. "You won't get a better learning experience anywhere else ... unless Stuttgart themselves sign you!"

The call for the players to take their places on the pitch came over the speakers, and Serge gave his dad a little wave as he strode over to his starting position for the team's first match of the day.

Serge was an attacking midfielder in the Kickers' U13s side. Even though he'd only just turned 11, he was their best player and the coach had built the entire team around him.

Within a few minutes of this first game it was obvious that the coach had made the right decision.

Serge had picked up the ball from deep, and one of the opposition defenders made the mistake of trying to close him down early.

Serge was too strong for the defender and quickly flicked the ball around him, before sprinting clear.

With a ball to chase in front of him, he was covering ground at an astonishing pace and moments later he was in the box, smashing the ball as hard as he could towards the net.

GOAL!

"Seriously, you can't leave us, Serge!" Max shouted as he jogged over to celebrate their fantastic start.

"I wouldn't be so sure about that," another team-mate chimed in. "I heard Coach saying there's some scouts hanging around."

Serge's eyes lit up.

He spent the rest of the day putting away goal after goal, at the same time hoping that every scout in Germany was here, their eyes all fixed on him.

His goals, however, weren't enough to help Stuttgarter Kickers win the tournament, and they were knocked out in the semi-finals.

Serge was gutted to have lost, but there was one silver lining that came with going out early – the chance to see the U18s final, and one player in particular.

Serge turned on his heels, ready to try to find which pitch the match was being held on, and bumped straight into his dad.

"Hold on, Serge, you're going to be disappointed," Jean-Hermann said, reading his son's mind. "I was speaking to some of the parents and Mesut's not playing today."

"What? How come?" Serge asked.

"He was snapped up by Schalke after last year."

"Wow," Serge said, though he wasn't entirely surprised. Any scouts here last year would have spotted him straight away.

As if on cue, Serge suddenly noticed a man striding towards them.

"You must be Serge?" the man said with a smile. He turned to Jean-Hermann and shook his hand. "My name's Hans. I work for Stuttgart."

Serge's mouth dropped open. "*Actual* Stuttgart?" he gasped.

"Yes, actual Stuttgart," Hans chuckled. "We'd like to talk to you and your dad about the possibility of you joining us at the *actual* Stuttgart Academy next season."

Serge looked around hastily to see if any of his team-mates were watching. This was something they'd only been joking about a few hours ago, but now he really was being offered the chance to go to one of the most famous football academies in Germany.

"Yes," Serge babbled. "Definitely. Absolut – "

"What he means," Jean-Hermann interrupted, "is that we'll think about it."

Serge stared up at his dad in disbelief. Surely he wasn't going to make him say no to this?

As his dad pocketed the scout's business card and started to steer his son back towards their car, Serge made a quick mental list of all the reasons why his dad couldn't stop him from going.

One: he'd already said 'no' to Bayern Munich – so he couldn't say no again.

Two: he couldn't play the 'too young' card, now that Serge was a *whole year* older.

Three: Stuttgart was local, unlike Bayern, so Serge could carry on living at home.

And four: Stuttgart Academy had produced players such as Mario Gómez and Kevin Kuranyi. Surely his dad didn't want to stop him becoming the next Kevin Kurányi?

"I can hear your brain ticking away, Serge," Jean-Hermann said, "and I just want you to know that I've already made my decision."

He paused and crouched down, so he was at eye-level with his son. "We both know you have what it takes for an academy, and I appreciate that this one is close to home … " He paused again. " … so I think you should do it."

Overcome with excitement, Serge jumped at his dad, giving him a big hug and knocking him to the ground.

"But … I think we'd better ask your mum what she thinks too!" Jean-Hermann laughed.

4

ACTUAL STUTTGART

June 2010, Stuttgart training ground, Stuttgart

"Josh!" Serge yelled, his voice carrying over the shouts of the rest of the players on the Stuttgart Academy training pitch. "Cross it!"

Joshua Kimmich skipped past the man in front of him and whipped the ball into the box – but he failed to hit it cleanly and the ball skimmed off the wet turf.

An opposition defender who was two metres closer to

the ball than Serge started to move towards it, but Serge reacted more quickly – and his speed got him to the ball first.

Shrugging off the defender's challenge, he used a second touch to take himself into the box.

Without hesitation he smashed the ball high into the top of the net, then turned and pointed at Joshua, a wide smile lighting up his face.

"You need to improve your crossing, man. I can't always save the day when you mess up!"

"I knew you'd get there, Serge," Joshua said with a grin, jogging over to him and holding his hand out for a high-five. "You're always the fastest player on the pitch. I just like giving you an extra bit of work to do!"

"Well, I *was* a sprinter. Probably could have gone to the Olympics," Serge shrugged, "won a few golds."

"Shut up, no you couldn't," Joshua scoffed, not believing Serge at all.

It was always good-natured, but all the kids at Stuttgart's academy talked a big game, and Serge was one of the worst offenders.

"No, for real. I could have," Serge insisted. "I just

preferred football. Besides, Usain Bolt broke all the records. No way was I going to bother after that."

"So you think you're going to break all the records in football instead?" Timo Werner laughed, drifting over to join them.

"Well, I reckon I've got a better chance than with running," Serge said, winking at his friends.

Serge had now been at Stuttgart Academy for four years and he, Joshua and Timo were unofficially the best players there.

Serge loved everything about the place – the friends he'd made, the competitive atmosphere and the feeling of being part of a club that was flying high in the Bundesliga.

And even though he wouldn't admit it to any of his mates, being close to home was a huge bonus for him.

It meant that he could see his dad every night – and tell him about everything that was going on, share his (few) disappointments and get a different perspective on his football.

Serge was naturally quick, but speed on its own wasn't enough. The coaches at the academy were teaching him how to read the game better, so that he could use his speed more effectively. From the very first day he walked out on to one of the academy pitches, they'd seen him as being on the wing. Now they were set on turning him into a *lethal* winger.

"Are you still coming to mine later?" Timo asked Serge as they started to make their way off the pitch.

Serge nodded eagerly. He'd been looking forward to Germany's opening match of the 2010 World Cup for weeks now – he was convinced it was going to be *their* year.

"He wouldn't miss it, Timo, he's too in love with Mesut Özil!" Joshua said. "And I don't even think Özil's that good, you know."

The trio were soon deep in discussion about the ins and outs of the German national squad, with each of them having their own strong opinion about the exact formation and players that Joachim Löw should pick for his starting eleven.

Come the evening, Serge sat in front of the TV with a

smile on his face, watching Germany dominate Australia – with Mesut Özil leading the charge.

"Still think he's not that good?" he asked Joshua, who was sitting across the living room.

"Well, he didn't score. Müller scored."

"Uh … we would not have won 4-0 without him," Serge protested, playfully throwing a cushion at Joshua.

"Yes we would have," Joshua said, throwing it back. "Because he's just like you, Serge. All sizzle, no steak. Give me a number nine who scores goals every day of the week, with no fancy flicks, no showing off."

The three boys started laughing, then wistfully carried on watching the German team's celebrations.

"Do you think we'll ever get into the squad?' Timo said softly. "That's surely the aim of all this – to play for Germany."

Serge couldn't answer for the others, but he felt quietly confident about his own chances. After all, his skills had got him into that tournament where he'd seen Özil playing. He wasn't going to let international competitions like the World Cup or the Euros be any different.

5

WENGER'S VISIT

June 2010, Stuttgart training ground, Stuttgart

With the World Cup still fresh in his mind, Serge had spent the whole of the day's training session pretending to be Mesut Özil whenever he raced in on goal.

Over and over again he happily imagined a stadium full of Germany fans – all on their feet, frantically waving German flags in the air.

But this time, as he got the ball into the box, he

wasn't going to score just *any* World Cup goal. This time he was on the verge of slamming home the winning goal for Germany in the World Cup Final.

The crowd was chanting his name. "SERGE! SERGE! SERGE!"

Suddenly, the sound of his name being called changed. It wasn't the World Cup crowd any more – it was just a single voice.

"Serge! Serge! Get over here!"

He turned and jogged towards Klaus Hubrich, one Stuttgart's youth coaches, who was calling him over.

"The head of the academy wants to see you," Klaus said, gesturing to a building near the first team's training ground.

"The head?" Serge asked, slightly confused. "Why?" He was sure he couldn't be about to get a professional contract, because he was still only fifteen. Did they want him to start training with the U21 squad?

Klaus shrugged and Serge instantly took off to the office.

Serge gasped when he saw the man who was waiting there for him.

"It's good to meet you, Serge," the man said, holding out his hand. "I'm Arsène Wenger."

"I know," Serge said abruptly, as he shook the hand of one of the greatest managers on the planet, "you're … you're … *here?*" he stuttered.

"He's here to sign you, Serge," the head of the academy said from behind his desk.

Until that moment Serge hadn't even realised that anybody else was in the room. But now, with a confused look on his face, Serge turned to stare at the academy official.

"Arsène has been reviewing our academy players," the official continued with a smile. "He thinks you'd be a great fit for Arsenal, back in England. In fact, we've already agreed a fee, so now it's just up to you." He paused, then added, "Of course, you'll need to get everything sorted with your family and so on."

"Can I … ?" Serge blurted out. He took a deep breath to control his excitement and made his next sentence a full one. "I thought I was too young."

"Well, you won't *actually* be able to come and join us until you turn sixteen," Arsène explained. "But, if we get it all agreed now, you will effectively be an Arsenal player straightaway."

Now Serge's head was spinning. This was exactly how all the stories about top players went – they started off playing in local clubs, then got scouted for an academy, and then they were signed up by a big team. A team like Arsenal.

Serge tried to slow things down in his mind, the way his dad always told him to, to think about the logistics of the decision.

He'd already talked about this kind of situation with his parents, about what would happen if a club that wasn't local came asking about him. His dad had always said that he'd go wherever Serge's football took him.

Back then, they'd only really been thinking in terms of Germany, but he knew his dad would find a way to make a move to England work.

The Premier League was the biggest league in the world right now, with English teams dominating the Champions League over the last few years. So when you were asked to go play in the Premier League, there was only one possible answer.

"Yes," Serge said firmly. "I'd love to go."

By the time Serge stumbled out of the office and started to look for Timo and Joshua, he was already dreaming about what would happen next.

Soon he'd be whisked into Arsenal's first team – then the trophies would start coming, and maybe then another big move would be on the table …

Serge spotted his friends practising keepie-uppies outside the first team's kit room, and rushed over to tell them his exciting news.

"This means you've only got one year left of me sorting out your miskicks, Josh!' Serge laughed. "So you'd better start improving!"

6
THE GUNNERS

July 2011, Arsenal training ground, London, England

As he walked around Arsenal's training ground, getting the full introductory tour and seeing everything from the gym to the canteen, Serge could hardly contain his excitement.

That certainly wasn't a new feeling. In fact, in the 12 months that had followed Arsène's visit to Stuttgart, Serge couldn't remember feeling any other way.

He'd been excited as he'd worked hard in training at the academy, thinking about how he was going to use everything he was learning to take the Premier League by storm.

And he'd been excited when he'd caught Arsenal's games on the TV and could see his future team-mates in action.

He quickly learnt, however, that excitement didn't make the time pass any more quickly. In fact, Serge was pretty sure that this had been the longest year of his life.

On the day that Serge found himself getting off the plane in England with his dad, he quickly discovered a whole new catalogue of things to get excited about.

He was excited to see that some of the things he'd heard about England were true. Despite the fact it was July, for example, there was a distinct chill in the air and some rainclouds were hanging in the distance.

"Hey, Dad, we might get some rain. It always rains in England!" he said.

He'd been excited to use his English – especially as he'd been working hard on it for a year.

And then, when they'd taken the Underground to their new flat, he'd been excited to see someone sitting opposite them wearing an Arsenal shirt.

He'd instantly had the urge to go over and introduce himself, to explain that he was a 'Gunner' and that he'd be wearing that shirt on the pitch really soon.

Thankfully his dad had been one step ahead of him, putting a hand on his shoulder to keep him in his seat. His expression had been very clear – 'No Serge, leave him alone.'

But now Serge's introductory tour of Arsenal's training ground had led him to the kit room, where he'd pulled on his brand-new training kit. Suddenly the word 'excitement' was taking on a whole new meaning.

"It's preseason, so reserve players are mixing with the senior ones," a coaching assistant said. "Follow me, son."

Wide-eyed, Serge followed the assistant on to a pristine training pitch and found himself surrounded by superstars. To his right, Robin van Persie was firing left-footed shots at goal, each one landing in the top corner.

And to his left, he could see Andrey Arshavin and Aaron Ramsey pinging passes to each other.

"Timo and Josh are never going to believe this," he muttered under his breath.

Waved on by the coaching assistant, Serge slowly started getting involved in some of the drills that were going on, copying what the players around him were doing.

He found a lot of it surprisingly easy, and there was a brief moment when he thought he might be joining the first team in the next couple of weeks.

Then they started playing a game – and Serge realised the truth.

He was far from ready for the first team.

In the first minute he was knocked to the floor by Laurent Koscielny, and the Frenchman roughly pulled him back to his feet by his shirt, growling "Welcome to Arsenal, kid."

After that incident, Serge decided to avoid going in to too many challenges. Instead, he decided to focus on what he did best – sprinting.

The ball was played through on the right-hand side

and he sprinted clear. As he ran he could already picture himself slotting the ball into the back of the net, with all the superstars on the pitch clapping him and asking his name.

Then, out of nowhere, a player came flashing past, stealing the ball from Serge's feet as he overtook him.

"Who was that?" Serge asked, turning to Aaron Ramsey.

"That's Héctor," Ramsey replied, "Héctor Bellerín. He's another youth player."

When the game ended, Serge walked off the pitch feeling slightly dazed. He'd been the best player at his school, the best at all his childhood clubs and the best in Stuttgart's academy. But here, he wasn't even the quickest player – and *that* was his thing.

The realisation ignited a fire in his belly.

For the first time in his life, he'd met a real challenge in football. He decided he was ready to attack it head-on.

Arsenal was his home now, and he was going to get stuck in.

7
RACE TO FIRST

September 2012, Arsenal training ground, London

"OK, we'll run from here to the goal, as usual," Serge said, as he lined up next to Héctor Bellerín.

In his first year at Arsenal Serge had formed a deadly partnership with the Spanish right-back. The fact that they were both extremely quick meant that defenders simply couldn't catch them, and Serge had no doubt that this was why they'd recently been moved.

Now, instead of training with the under-eighteens, they were both training with the reserve and senior squad.

Serge did a few of his usual lunges, preparing for their usual post-training race. He was definitely making progress at Arsenal, and thought he wasn't far off getting his professional debut – something he'd been obsessed with since first meeting Arsène in Stuttgart.

"You ready yet?" Héctor shouted.

"Always!" Serge shot back playfully. "You do the honours."

"Three … two … one … GO!" Hector shouted.

The two of them sped off, eating up the distance with ease. They remained neck-and-neck right up to the last few metres, when Serge managed to lengthen his stride and push himself just far enough ahead to get a hand on the goalpost first.

He was quick to turn and punch the air, confirming his victory to those players who'd hung back after the training session to watch the pair.

"Well, my ability is clearly rubbing off on you," Héctor panted, clapping him on the back. Serge knew that Héctor wasn't far wrong.

In fact, all the players he'd been mixing with at Arsenal were doing his game wonders, and his struggles on the first day now seemed like a distant memory.

He was sure, too, that having his dad around, living with him in England, was the other big reason he'd been able to settle and adjust to football at Arsenal so easily.

He'd felt really sorry for the young kids who didn't have anyone in London and had to deal with homesickness as well as football in such a sprawling city.

Suddenly, a movement at the sidelines caught Serge's eye. He put his hand to his forehead to block out the Autumn sun and saw that it was Arsène, and he was waving for him to come over.

Serge quickly jogged over to his manager.

"Congratulations on your little race," Arsène called out when Serge was within earshot.

Serge chuckled, not sure whether he should be embarrassed or proud. Luckily, the manager had already moved on to what he wanted to talk about.

"We've got a League Cup game against Coventry coming up," Arsène said, squinting at something in the distance. "I think it's an ideal opportunity to get some of the younger players used to a match-day. Not to mention the fact we've got a bit of an injury crisis on our hands."

He turned and looked at Serge, who was trying to work out if Arsène was saying what he thought he was saying. Even though he'd been expecting this, it still sounded too good to be true.

"Maybe you wouldn't mind helping us out, Serge?"

It took everything Serge had not to spring at the manager and give him a big hug, the way he'd hugged his dad when he'd said he could join Stuttgart.

Instead, he made sure he replied to the question as professionally as he could.

"Yeah, I can do that."

"It's so cool under the lights, isn't it?" Héctor whispered to Serge, as they both sat on the bench, soaking up the atmosphere of this League Cup match. True to his word, Arsène had put the two youngsters on the bench against Coventry.

Serge thought 'cool' was an understatement. Being in the Emirates Stadium, watching the home fans jumping to their feet whenever the ball was taken into the opposition's half, was simply incredible.

The fact that Arsenal already had a healthy three-goal lead only made it better.

Everything was in place for an ambitious young player to make his debut, and Serge kept glancing over to Arsène, hoping that his moment would come sooner rather than later.

Sure enough, in the middle of the second half he heard one of the coaching assistants shout the words he'd been waiting for.

"Gnabry – you're coming on!"

It was only going to be 18 minutes, but he was going to play for Arsenal.

At one moment he was fist-bumping Héctor and jumping to his feet, and then he was on the pitch, swapping places with Alex Oxlade-Chamberlain.

"Cheers Ox," he said, trying to sound cool *and* stay focused, but random thoughts kept popping into his head.

He wondered if the man he'd seen wearing an Arsenal shirt on the Tube, on his first day in London, was watching. He wondered what the commentators were saying about him. He wondered what his dad, who was sitting somewhere in the stands, was thinking.

Suddenly Serge felt some players flash past him.

The game was back underway.

Eagerly he started following the ball around the pitch, although he was struggling to make an impact. He wasn't involved when Theo Walcott raced clear and gave Arsenal a 4-0 lead.

And he wasn't involved in trying to stop Coventry as they clawed one back.

But within a few minutes, Serge had his head in the game.

He started to play his main role within the team, running at tired defenders, which was the best feeling in the world.

By the time the final whistle went, confirming Arsenal's 6-1 victory, Serge knew that it was a feeling he was already addicted to.

8
GOING FOR GAMES

April 2013, Arsenal training ground, London

Serge stood outside the door to Arsène's office, trying to build up the courage to knock on it.

After his debut against Coventry in the League Cup, he'd also played debut games in the Premier League and the Champions League, as well as another hour in the League Cup.

He'd been confident that this early flurry of

appearances meant that he was going to be playing a role in the first team over the course of the season – but it hadn't happened that way.

Arsenal had recovered from their injury crisis and every time Serge looked at the teamsheet for an upcoming game, he'd see his name left off, with other wingers at the club listed instead.

Seeing Podolski or Walcott or Oxlade-Chamberlain or Gervinho's names on the sheet sometimes made his heart sink.

His dad had packed up his entire life to come to England with him, and Serge didn't want that to be for nothing. But, more than anything, seeing the other names on the sheet made him feel as if he was being teased.

Having experienced the incredible feeling of being out on the pitch with the first team, it was now doubly disappointing not to be getting game time.

Serge couldn't just lie down and accept that, so he took a deep breath, knocked on the door in front of him, opened it and walked into the office.

He was surprised to see how plain the room was – just

some empty shelves lining the walls and two brown leather sofas facing each other.

Arsène was sitting on one of the sofas. He smiled and gestured for Serge to come over.

Serge started pleading his case before he'd even sat down, but as soon as Arsène realised what Serge was asking for, he interrupted him.

"You're not ready," the manager said calmly.

"Just on the bench," Serge begged. "Give me five minutes to … "

Arsène held his hand up, cutting Serge off.

Getting in the way of players who just wanted to be doing what they loved was one of the worst parts of being a manager. Arsène was really fond of Serge – the way he was in such a rush to progress was quite endearing – but the manager had a club to run.

"I'm sorry, Serge, but we're in a real battle for the Champions League spots and I can't afford to take any risks with a practically untested player." He paused to let it sink in. "Have another year of under-23 football, and then next year we can talk."

Serge wished his manager hadn't made such a

reasonable point. This was how conversations with his dad always went. Serge always wanted to be able to disagree with him, to keep pushing for his chance, but deep down he knew that he'd probably make exactly the same choice if he was in Arsène's position.

So Serge just nodded, thanked the manager for his time and left the office.

"No luck?" said Héctor, who'd been waiting for him around the corner.

Serge's face quickly answered the question, as he swept past his friend.

"Well, it was worth a shot," Héctor went on, trying to catch him up. "Don't worry, I'm in the same boat."

Serge suddenly stopped in his tracks. The frustration on his face had already disappeared and had been replaced with a look of fierce determination.

"We're just going to have to get so good that Arsène has no choice but to play us."

He turned to Héctor, putting both hands on his friend's shoulders. "Soon it will be me and you, tearing up that wing."

9
REUNITED IN RED

September 2013, Arsenal training ground, London

Serge paced excitedly up and down the corridor outside Arsenal's gym.

When he'd first heard the name of the club's latest £42 million signing, he simply hadn't believed it. Even now, it seemed more like one of his Stuttgart Academy daydreams than real life.

He quickly scuttled back over to the door to the gym

and peered through the little window, as if to confirm to himself that it wasn't all just a big rumour.

It wasn't.

He could see him with his own eyes – Mesut Özil, fresh from Real Madrid, was wrapping up his physical examination. He was the talisman that Arsenal were going to build their team around.

After spending a few seconds preparing himself, Serge pushed the door open and started to make his way over to his idol, as casually as he could manage.

"Hey man," he said, his voice breaking slightly. He nervously cleared his throat before asking the question he'd been rehearsing all morning. "How are you finding things?"

"Good thanks. It's a great club isn't it?" Mesut replied, looking around the room and nodding as he spoke. "And there's a lot of Germans here now."

"Yeah, it's brilliant," Serge said eagerly. "I'm Serge by the way."

He paused, wondering whether to say what was on the tip of his tongue. He didn't want to embarrass himself, and he knew that Héctor would tease him mercilessly, but the words were already cascading out of his mouth.

"I don't know if you know this, but I met you at the youth tournament you used to play in – the one back in Stuttgart. We took a picture together."

"No way!" Mesut said, genuinely excited. "I remember the tournament, but I don't remember seeing you, Serge. You must have been so young back then."

"Yeah, I was only 10."

The fact that he was now standing in Arsenal's gym, in London, chatting with Mesut Özil was boggling Serge's mind.

It only seemed like yesterday that he'd been watching Mesut at the World Cup, with Timo and Josh. They would be beside themselves when they saw him playing on the pitch alongside the German legend.

As he stood there, Serge decided that that day would come sooner rather than later.

After all, his plan to improve so much that Arsène would *have* to choose him was starting to work. His year of U23 football had already included being on the bench for the first team a couple of times – he just needed to keep his foot on the pedal, and rubbing shoulders with his hero every day would give him just the boost he needed.

Sure enough, three weeks later Serge was named in Arsenal's starting eleven for the first time in his career.

He'd felt a wave of satisfaction as he'd walked on to the pitch, but that had been replaced with a feeling of disappointment by the time he'd trudged off it at the end of the game.

It had been a tough match against a good Stoke side, and he'd not been hugely involved in Arsenal's victory. If he wanted to seal his place on the teamsheet, he knew he needed to make a bigger impact.

And now, after being handed his second start in a match against Swansea, Arsène's half-time team talk was giving him a good idea of how to go about it.

It had been a dull first half and the score was stuck at 0-0.

"This is the kind of game that champions take three

points from, lads," Arsène announced. "We just need that first goal to put us in the driving seat!"

By the time Serge was marching back out onto the pitch, he had made his mind up. Whatever it took, he would score.

Only 13 minutes later the ball was flicked over to him by Aaron Ramsey, and he found himself just inside the box. What happened next was completely instinctive. His first touch trapped the ball, and with his second he slid it into the bottom corner.

GOAL!

As Serge started racing toward the corner flag, he felt as if he was glowing. He'd scored his first professional goal – *and* he'd just broken the deadlock, just as Arsène had asked.

He only managed to catch a quick glimpse of the manager's celebrations before his team-mates piled on top of him. Amongst all the shouts of praise and the roars of the fans, one voice stood out.

"Great goal, Serge."

Overwhelmed, Serge could only give Mesut a little nod in return.

10
GOALS AND CROSSES

January 2014, Arsenal training ground, London

Every time Serge looked at the teamsheet and saw that he was starting on the bench, he'd let out an impatient sigh.

He'd assumed that his goal at Swansea – together with the few he'd scored in U21 and U23 games – would have got his career at Arsenal moving. But that wasn't the case.

In fact, it began to feel as if his career was going backwards, as most of his appearances were now coming at the ends of matches, in five- or ten-minute cameos.

Serge couldn't make sense of it. He'd scored in his second start and he was now the second-youngest Premier League goalscorer for Arsenal, behind Cesc Fàbregas. What was going on?

As he walked on to the training pitch for the day's training session, he wondered whether Arsène just wanted to see another goal from him. Perhaps the manager wanted proof that he could be consistent.

"How am I supposed to score if I only get 10 minutes on the pitch and I spend all that time out on the wing," he muttered to himself, feeling dispirited.

He heard a laugh behind him and turned to see Mesut standing there.

Though it was sometimes quite surreal, for Serge at least, the two had actually become good friends in the last few months. Mesut was not only very laid-back company, but as a more experienced player he was also full of good advice.

"Why do you want to score goals?" Mesut asked, curious.

Serge was going to reply, then stopped himself. Why *did* he want to score goals? It was a very good question.

Yes, it felt good – his one against Swansea had showed him that, but what he *really* wanted was to be out on the pitch, playing top-level football. He'd always just assumed that getting goals was the way to make that happen.

"Obviously it's nice to get one, but if you're stuck out wide you should work on your crossing," Mesut continued, filling the silence. "Setting up goals for other people gets the same end result for the team."

Serge couldn't argue with that. Mesut was right, of course. Creating opportunities for other players to score would make it just as clear that he was an essential part of the team. And, anyway, crossing was a key part of being a winger. He certainly didn't want to neglect it.

Mesut suddenly strode towards a trolley filled with footballs at the side of the training pitch, then pushed it over to the left of the box, just a few metres out.

Serge followed him.

"There's a few different types of crosses you can do," Mesut said, as he picked up one of the footballs. "The one you choose should depend on who's in the box."

"Well, what would you do for Giroud?" Serge asked. He was already hanging on to Mesut's every word.

"Giroud is quite tall and he's got a good header, so you want to do a high cross, often a bit slower."

Mesut placed the ball he was holding on the floor in front of him and showed Serge exactly what he meant, lofting it into the box.

"Or, if you don't have as much time to pick a man out, you could do a faster, whipped cross – just fire it into the six-yard box." Again, he picked up a ball and demonstrated what he was describing.

Serge was delighted to realise he'd definitely done a few of those crosses himself, just on instinct.

"Yeah, those come quite naturally to me. I like to fizz it in. It panics the defenders and keepers," he said with a grin.

"Exactly," Mesut said, clearly enjoying giving the lesson just as much as Serge was enjoying listening to it. "Any touch and it might go in. Now, the best place to put a cross is in between the keeper and defenders. You want it far enough away from the keeper so that he can't come out and catch it, but not too close to the defenders so that they can head it clear."

Mesut picked another ball out of the trolley, but this time he handed it to Serge, encouraging him to have a go.

II
THE TWIST

April 2014, Arsenal training ground, London

Serge expertly crossed a ball into the box, then gave Mesut a cheeky little smile across the training pitch.

With Mesut's advice and all the effort he was putting into training, Serge was steadily getting more and more game time.

He'd had 69 minutes against Aston Villa, 71 minutes against Fulham and 70 minutes against Southampton.

It did really feel as if everything was coming together – and not just for him. Arsenal were on the verge of a cup final, and seeing a possible end to the club's recent trophy drought was certainly improving the atmosphere in training.

"Serge! To you," one of the strikers in the box yelled.

Still smiling, Serge stretched for the ball that had just been played behind him, when suddenly he felt his knee twist beneath him.

The pain was so intense that he just screamed, slumping to the floor in a crumpled heap.

Like any footballer, Serge had pulled and strained his fair share of muscles, but as he lay on the grass right now he knew that this was something else – something worse.

He felt vomit rise up his throat and he quickly swallowed it back down, closing his eyes as he tried to concentrate on anything other than the shooting pain in his leg.

He could hear his team-mates' voices around him.

"Quick, get the physio!"

"It's OK, Serge, somebody's on their way."

He didn't dare look down at his knee until he was

lying on the physio bed in the club's medical room, and he was shocked to see how swollen it was.

"I think you've done your cruciate ligaments," the physio said with a grim look on his face. It was a look that told Serge everything he needed to know about the seriousness of the injury.

Serge tried to listen to the physio as his mind went into overdrive. Well, this is a shame, he thought, but he'd be back on the pitch in a few weeks. Perhaps he'd even get a few more appearances in before the end of the season.

Serge could see the physio's lips moving, and he tried to focus on what he was saying, even though he was starting to feel a little dizzy.

"Now, we won't know for sure until we've done some scans, but from experience I think you're going to be out for eight to nine months, possibly longer."

Serge awoke from his dream and sat bolt upright in bed. In the months since picking up his knee injury, he'd been having this same dream over and over again.

In the dream, he is at the start of the race. Some of the boys from Stuttgart are on his left – Josh and Timo are definitely there – and some of the lads from Arsenal, including Héctor, are on his right.

They're all just getting into position, then a gun fires and everyone takes off – everyone except Serge. He's moving his legs as fast as he can, but it's as if he's glued to the spot. He can see everyone else getting further and further away from him … and then he wakes up.

The first time he'd had this dream was the night he'd watched Arsenal lift the FA Cup. He'd wanted to be with his team-mates when they'd celebrated the end of their trophy drought, but he'd been forced to watch from home, on the TV.

He'd had another setback four months into his slow rehabilitation, in a recovery session in the USA. He'd been on a treadmill, thinking that he was just starting to find his rhythm, when his knee had suddenly slipped from under him.

Once again, the news from the physio had been devastating. This time, it might be another year before he'd be playing football again.

Serge hated being off the pitch, knowing his fitness was falling away, but really the worst thing was the loneliness he felt.

He'd spent most of his life in football clubs and academies, enjoying the competitive fun and banter that came with hanging out with a group of lads all day, every day. But now, stuck in his bed at home, he felt as if he was in a little team of one.

The noise coming from outside his bedroom quickly reminded him that he wasn't alone. At the very least he was, and always would be, in a team of two – with his dad.

Serge made his way to the kitchen, where he found his breakfast waiting for him. Taking a seat, he decided to say the one thing he'd been too scared to say to anybody since he'd left the physio's office on crutches.

"Dad, they're not going to bring me back into the team."

Jean-Hermann looked at his son. He hated seeing him so deflated over these past few months, but he was happy to hear Serge finally talking about what was on his mind.

It was progress, and it meant that Jean-Hermann could do the one job he'd been doing since Serge was a little boy – stopping his mind racing away with itself, and getting him to think about things in a different way.

"You've been at that club for three years, Serge," Jean-Hermann replied gently. "Arsène knows what you can do – and he trusts you."

"They've already bought Alexis Sánchez," Serge said, starting to push the eggs his dad had cooked for him around his plate with a fork. He was sick of all the protein-rich foods he had to eat to help him maintain his muscle mass.

"He's from Barcelona," he went on. "I can't compete with that."

"That's a good thing. Another world-class winger you can learn from."

"But what if I lose my pace?" Serge asked desperately, dropping his fork onto his plate.

It was the one big question that had been burning constantly in his mind, as his pace was one of the things that set him apart from most wingers. He knew that players often struggled to return from injuries like this with the same speed that they'd had before.

"Do you remember your first day at Arsenal?" his dad asked him quietly.

Serge frowned, wondering what his dad was talking about.

"When you got home, you told me everyone was better than you – but they wouldn't be for long. You didn't let it throw you, and you're a better player for it. Overcoming this," he gestured towards Serge's knee, "will have exactly the same result. Work hard and you'll get your pace back. You might even be stronger than before."

It was exactly what Serge needed to hear, and Jean-Hermann could already see a glint in his son's eye as he started to eat his eggs.

12
FROM ALONE TO ON LOAN

July 2015, Arsenal training ground, London

Serge sat outside Arsène's office, waiting to see the manager. He was feeling rather proud of himself.

In the past year Serge had seen enough physios, treadmills and sports rehabilitation centres to last him a lifetime, but he'd done it – he'd recovered his fitness, and had got himself back to the brink of first team football once again. He had even played in a few preseason friendlies for the Arsenal first team.

Still, Serge was quite nervous about this meeting with Arsène. The manager had asked to see him, but he had no idea why. His fitness wasn't quite back to where it had been – was Arsène going to let him go?

After all, a lot had changed at Arsenal in his absence. For one, Arsenal had lifted the FA Cup for a second year running – and Héctor had helped them do it. In Serge's absence Héctor had become a big part of the first team.

For a moment the thought brought Serge's recurring dream flooding back, and he winced. The same thing had happened when he'd found out that Joshua had been snapped up by Bayern Munich and that Timo was now playing regularly for Stuttgart in the Bundesliga.

But Serge was learning to manage his impulses and this time, just as before, he'd shrugged it all off. He was genuinely thrilled for Héctor, and he reached for his phone to read through the messages they'd sent each other after Arsenal's FA Cup win.

> You were immense, bro. You might even beat me in a race at the moment!

Thanks Serge. I just wish we'd been tearing up the wing together, like we always used to say.

The door to the office suddenly opened and Serge looked up to see Arsène beaming at him.

"It's good to see you, Serge. Thank you for coming in," Arsène said, inviting him to take a seat on that same old brown leather sofa. Then he sat himself down opposite Serge.

"I just wanted to tell you in person that we're so glad you're back on your feet – and you can rest assured that your future at Arsenal is safe."

Serge felt a surge of relief.

"I'm just not sure that we're going to have space for you in the squad this year," Arsène continued. "I do, however, want you to build up your first-team experience, so I'm looking to loan you out for a year. How does that sound?"

Serge looked at Arsène. This wasn't quite what he'd been expecting, especially after the way the conversation had started. After such a long time away, he'd really been looking forward to getting back to playing with Héctor, Mesut, and all his other friends at Arsenal.

But Arsène was right – Serge needed first-team experience, and even before his injury he'd been struggling to get enough of that at Arsenal.

"OK," Serge said eventually. "Where do you think I should go?"

"West Brom," Arsène replied brightly. "They're doing quite well in the league, and I think you'll play a lot of football there."

A smile spread across Serge's face. Playing 'a lot football' was all he'd ever wanted to do.

13
WEST BROM'S SOFTIE

August 2015, West Bromwich Albion training ground,
West Bromwich

Serge raced across the Hawthorns' turf, collected the ball and started to turn – just as Gareth McAuley clattered into him.

He collapsed to the floor and instinctively reached for his bad knee. He really hoped that it hadn't gone again. He wasn't sure he could cope with further injury – he'd been working on his recovery for so long already.

"Get on your feet, son!" West Brom manager Tony Pulis bellowed from the sideline. "You might get to roll around at Arsenal, but we don't do that here."

Serge looked over at him, surprise no doubt showing on his face. Did Tony know he'd just come back from a really serious knee injury?

Saido Berahino quickly helped him to his feet. "Don't worry about the gaffer," he said, smiling, "he talks a big game, but he's not all that bad."

Serge nodded back. He'd really wanted to impress in this first training session, but it couldn't be any clearer that Tony thought he was some Arsenal softie who couldn't cut it at West Brom.

Nevertheless he kept going and got stuck in to all the drills the rest of the team were doing.

Getting the manager onside was just another challenge he needed to tackle head-on. Then he could start playing so well that Arsenal would be forced to call him back.

Serge also knew he had a lot of work to do to adjust to West Brom's style of play.

While Arsenal had been all about passing the ball

along the floor, West Brom used long balls over the top, and Tony wanted Serge to use his pace – and only his pace – to get behind the defenders.

So after the session drew to a close and the other players started to leave for the day, Serge stayed on the training pitch. It was a light summer evening and he wanted to get a few extra fitness drills in.

Serge wasn't surprised to find himself starting on the bench for the West Brom's first Premier League game of the season.

Even before announcing the team for the game, Tony had said that he wanted James McClean and Callum McManaman on the wings, because they were the two hardest workers in the squad. It had been a bit of a kick in the teeth for Serge, but he'd not let it show.

"Maybe I'd have a better chance of a place if my name was Serge McGnabry," he'd joked to Victor Anichebe after the team meeting.

"You'll soon see that Tony has his favourites," Victor had replied with a chuckle.

Now, as Serge sat watching the game from the bench, he realised that Tony's 'favourites' weren't really up to it.

After missing an early penalty, West Brom were 3-1 down and were struggling against a strong Chelsea side that had won the league last year.

Things only started to look up when Chelsea went down to 10 men, and West Brom managed to reduce Chelsea's lead to a single goal.

At this point, Tony summoned Serge from the bench.

"Right, you," he said gruffly, "get out there and let's see if you can do anything."

But in his 12 minutes on the pitch, Serge struggled to get the ball, let alone do anything that made an impact.

It was frustrating not to be able to showcase any of his hard work from training, but he was sure he couldn't be blamed when he'd had so little time on the pitch.

He was wrong.

Tony didn't look at him as he came off after West Brom's disappointing 3-2 defeat was confirmed. He also didn't look at him as the team shuffled back into the dressing room.

Serge decided to keep his eyes on the floor as the manager gave the whole team a dressing down, only looking up when Tony bellowed that 'it wasn't anywhere near good enough.'

As Serge glanced up, he could see the manager looking directly at him.

14
SERGE'S SLATING

October 2015, Serge's home, West Bromwich

Serge sat staring at the TV in utter disbelief. He couldn't
figure out what he was hearing.

His phone had come alive with people texting him
about this press conference, but he thought they'd been
overreacting. Now he was watching it for himself.

"Serge has come here to play games, but so far he just
hasn't been, for me, at the level needed to play them."

Serge raised his hands to his face as he listened to the West Brom manager.

"Does academy football really prepare players for league football?" Tony Pulis went on, "and we're talking about Premier League football here. As a manager, you pick a team that's going to win a game of football. You pick your best team – "

Serge flicked the TV off, not wanting to hear another word. In fact, all he wanted right now was for the ground to swallow him up.

It was embarrassing enough that he hadn't played in the Premier League since that debut against Chelsea, with Tony consistently favouring his other wingers.

In fact, he'd only played twice more – in the League Cup – before being shoved into the reserves.

He'd seen some of the headlines in the media pick up on it, asking why West Brom weren't using the young superstar they'd brought in from Arsenal.

But now, for Pulis to be addressing those rumours so publicly, announcing that Serge wasn't good enough for Premier League football, suggesting that he was lazy, overweight …

It was yet another career disaster.

Serge quickly reached for his phone and rang Héctor. He had to know what Arsenal were making of all this.

"It's not true you know," he said desperately, before Héctor had even said hello.

"I know, man," Héctor replied.

"Has Wenger said anything?"

"I don't know, Serge, but I really wouldn't worry. Nobody at Arsenal is going to care what Tony Pulis thinks."

After the call Serge sat holding his phone, still unconvinced. He put the phone down next to him, then picked it up again and rang his dad.

"This wasn't how it was meant to go, Dad," Serge said, clearly sounding upset.

He wasn't talking just about West Brom. He was talking about all the knockbacks he'd experienced in his career, seeming to come one after the other.

"I was meant to be scouted, go to an academy, get signed to a big team, then easily break into their first team, get some trophies, and then it was only supposed to get better from there on."

He took a breath before continuing. "I suppose it's all just been delayed and – "

"Serge, listen," his dad interrupt, his voice sounding firm. He paused to give Serge a moment to focus, to stop talking and start listening.

"I know you've always been a sprinter," Jean-Hermann continued, "but it's not a sprint to the top. For most players, even the very, very best, it's a marathon, with more twists and turns than anybody thinks they deserve. But you will come out of this all the better for it. These setbacks make you stronger, and they make you *better*. Do you understand?"

Serge shook his head. His dad may have said the right thing after his injury, but he didn't want to hear what he was saying now.

Serge ended the call, took a deep breath and mentally prepared his own plan of attack. All he had to do was keep his head down until January. That was when this loan spell came to an end.

Then he could return to Arsenal and get everything back on track.

15
OLYMPIAN AT LAST

June 2016, Arsenal training ground, London

"I've got two words for you. The Olympics."

Serge gripped his phone tightly and grinned as he listened to Germany's U21 manager, Horst Hrubesch.

"This is actually going to be the first German squad at the Olympics since we became one country again," Horst continued, "so it's a big one. Plus, we're World

Champions now, so we've already got a bit of a reputation for winning tournaments in Brazil."

When Serge had returned to Arsenal in January, the club had been in another battle to confirm their Champions League spot, so he'd had to join the U21 team for the rest of the season.

It had been such an embarrassment, so to be getting news like this was an incredible lift.

Not only did a team want him – a national side at that – but he was also being given a chance to remind the football world of his talent, and he was going to grab that chance with both hands.

"I can't wait, Horst," Serge said firmly. "And I'm not going to let you down."

The flight to Brazil had been more fun than Serge had expected. He was the only player in the squad who didn't play club football in Germany, so he thought he'd be the odd one out, but it hadn't felt like that at all.

Because the Olympics was effectively a youth tournament – each team was only allowed to have three players over the age of 23 – Serge actually recognised many of his team-mates because he'd played alongside them in the Germany U16s team during his time at Stuttgart.

He knew team captain Leon Goretzka, for example – who'd saved him a seat.

"You've gotta sit here, Serge. I need to know everything about Wenger! What's he like?"

Serge had spent most of the flight chatting and cracking jokes with Leon, the Bender twins, Niklas Süle and Max Meyer. By the time they landed in Brazil, they were all behaving like long-lost friends.

The real fun, however, had started in the tournament itself. It had been a tough first game against Mexico, a team who had a high-quality U23 side, but Serge had scored a goal, helping Germany keep them to a draw.

Then he'd scored another two goals against South Korea, two against Fiji and one against Portugal.

When he didn't score in their 2-0 win over Nigeria, his team-mates couldn't keep quiet.

"Were you even on the pitch, Serge?"

"Big semi-final and you go missing, eh?"

Serge cheerfully laughed it all off. All that mattered was that Germany were into the final.

Serge stood in the heat of the Macarenã Stadium, looking at the Brazilian team that Germany were about to take on in the Olympics final. For once, no one on the German team was laughing.

Two years earlier, Germany had thrashed Brazil 7-1 and knocked them out of their own World Cup. Then they'd gone on to win the tournament in this very stadium.

Now Gabriel Jesus, Marquinhos, Rafinha and Felipe Anderson wanted revenge in front of their home fans, and the Brazilian team were being captained by the biggest player at the tournament – Neymar.

The first goal in the game came after half an hour, when Brazil were awarded a free kick on the edge of the box.

Neymar took it, and everyone just stood and watched as he fired it towards the goal, the ball elegantly clipping the crossbar and landing in the back of the net.

"*That's* the level I want to be at," Serge muttered, despite being unable to hear himself over the deafening noise of the Brazilian fans.

In the second half, Germany had more of the game. A flowing move down the right-hand side got the ball over to Max Meyer, who smashed it into the bottom corner, bringing Germany level.

For the next hour Serge chased every ball, fought every challenge and made every cross he could – but even after extra time the teams remained deadlocked at 1-1.

The final was going to a penalty shootout – with an Olympic gold medal on the line.

Serge was second up, and he put his penalty away comfortably. Slipping back into line with his team-mates, he knew there was nothing more he could possibly do, except watch with bated breath.

One by one, every player put their penalty away, until it came to Nils Petersen, who saw his penalty saved by the Brazilian keeper. Now all Neymar had to do to win it for Brazil was to score.

He did so with ease.

It pained Serge to watch the Brazilians celebrating their victory. He could feel that his team-mates were just as frustrated as he was to have come so close, but standing in line, ready to collect his silver medal, a small smile crept back onto his face.

"What are you so happy about?" Nils Petersen muttered, standing next to him.

"When I was a kid, everyone thought I could go to the Olympics as a sprinter," Serge told him. "Now look at me! I'm an Olympic medallist alright – and it's for football!"

16
MOVING ON

August 2016, Olympic Village, Rio de Janeiro, Brazil

"Serge, I just had to call and congratulate you on how well you've done at the Olympics."

Sitting on his bed in the Olympic village in Rio, Serge listened with pleasure to Arsène's praise over the phone.

He'd had the best few weeks in Brazil – being around all the German lads, losing himself in the football and finishing as the top goalscorer of the tournament.

And now, finding out that he'd shown the Arsenal manager what an important player he could be was the final flourish.

"Now the Prem has already restarted," Arsène went on, "I want to get you signed back on to a new contract as soon as we can."

"Really?" Serge replied excitedly. He'd half-forgotten that his five-year contract was nearly up. "So am I going to be part of the squad for this season?"

There was a long pause.

"Well, I don't know if we're *quite* ready to find a regular place for you this season," Arsène said finally. "But with another year of U23 football under your belt, there could very well be next season."

Arsène's reply forced Serge to confront a possibility that had been in his mind for some time.

Ever since his very first training session at Arsenal, he'd always thought of the club as his home. He'd learned so much there and he knew his way around the training ground as well as anybody. Everybody from the kit man to the canteen staff – they all felt like family.

But Serge was now twenty one years old, and he'd

only played 21 first-team games. He realised that, if he stayed at Arsenal, that wasn't going to change quickly.

He remembered his conversation with his dad after the Tony Pulis incident. Serge had always seen himself as moving swiftly along a set path to get to the pinnacle of his football career – but perhaps that path no longer included Arsenal.

After a long pause, Serge spoke up. "I'm sorry, boss, but I don't think that's going to work for me." He was surprised by how calm he sounded.

"Serge," Arsène began, but Serge didn't want to give his manager a chance to talk him out of this.

For Serge, it was suddenly crystal clear.

To move forward and get the chance to play top-level football, he had to step away from the prestige of this club. He had to start taking a different route to the top.

"I actually want to try and sort out a permanent move."

There was a long pause.

"If you change your mind, then give me a call,"

Arsène said evenly. There was a click and Serge found himself listening to dialling tone.

For a few minutes Serge just sat there, processing what he'd just done. Then he picked up the phone and called his agent. His time with the Olympic squad had given him a pretty good idea of where he wanted to be playing.

"Have you heard from any German clubs?" he pressed, after he'd told his agent about his conversation with Arsène.

"Well, Werder Bremen are really interested in you," his agent replied. He started to explain that the club were currently mid-table in the Bundesliga, looking to make a return to the European scene, but Serge had already heard enough.

Werder Bremen had been one of the stops on Mesut Özil's path to greatness.

Now Serge was going to follow in his footsteps. He was going to show the likes of Arsène Wenger and Tony Pulis just what he was capable of.

17
HOME FROM HOME

November 2016, Werder Bremen training ground
Bremen, Germany

As Serge finished his training session with Werder Bremen, he could feel all eyes on him as he walked back to the dressing rooms.

"Everything OK, guys?" he asked, feeling a little self-conscious.

Manager Alexander Nouri was the first to speak. "I've just got off the phone with Joachim Löw.

He's looking to try out some new players for the German senior team's next match. He wants you in his squad, son."

Serge stopped in his tracks. He wondered if he'd misheard what his new manager had said, or if his brain had replaced something mundane with the kind of thing he'd always dreamed of hearing.

But then a call up to the national team wasn't entirely out of the question. The German senior squad hadn't got beyond the semi-finals of the 2016 Euros, which for them was a massive disappointment, so they would be keen to bring in some fresh blood. And Serge was a tried and trusted youth player.

He'd also been flourishing at Werder Bremen in the last few months. He was getting plenty of game time, which meant that he was gaining experience and learning to deal with the intensity of live matches better than ever before. It was still only November and he already had four Bundesliga goals and an assist under his belt this season.

"Hey Serge! You listening?" Alexander shouted. "I said, you've been called up to the national team!"

Even then the message didn't hit home, until all the people around him started to congratulate him. Serge tried to thank everyone, but he was struggling to get the words out. He was already thinking about pulling on his Germany shirt and making his country proud.

Serge was warming up for his first training session with the German squad when he heard a familiar voice behind him.

"Well, well, well. Look what Joachim's dragged in."

He turned to see Joshua Kimmich's smiling face and suddenly he felt as if he was 12 years old again, running rampant at Stuttgart Academy.

"I knew we'd be playing for Germany together one day," Joshua said, as he hugged Serge. "Now we just need Timo here!"

Serge's first game for his country was against minnows San Marino.

It was great to be back on the pitch with Josh, but

Serge had worried that playing amongst legends such as Thomas Müller, Mario Gómez and Mats Hummels might throw him off his game. But in fact the opposite was true – playing alongside them was making him feel unstoppable.

Sami Khedira had already put Germany ahead in the first five minutes, and only two minutes later Serge found the ball rebounding towards him on the edge of the box. He decided to curl it into the far corner.

GOAL!

Seeing the ball nestled in the back of the net was a feeling like no other, but Serge held his celebrations in check. Scoring was just another day at the office for this team, and he wanted to fit in with the superstars.

So he decided to copy what Sami had done a few minutes before, coolly spinning on his heels to go and restart the game. But then he noticed Mats Hummels coming over to give him a hug.

Serge smiled – clearly they still knew how much a goal on your international debut meant.

"Congratulations, kid," Mats said. "But I reckon there's even more goals in this for you."

Sure enough, after Jonas Hector had got another for the team, Serge tucked a ball home from a Joshua Kimmich cross to make it 4-0.

Again, he contained his utter elation at having scored, and just casually retrieved the ball from the back of the net, as if scoring a brace on your international debut was no big feat.

"Bet you've missed my crosses," Joshua shouted, as Serge sped past him to get back into position.

Serge grinned but didn't bother replying. His mind was now focused on the next thing – adding his name to the elite list of players who'd scored hat-tricks for Germany on their debuts.

And, after Jonas Hector added a fifth, Serge did just that, volleying in a Thomas Müller cross.

This time, Serge couldn't hold back his smile as he high-fived his team-mates. Between his achievement today and the knowledge he was returning to Werder Bremen – a club that was fully behind him and could see his potential – he felt as if he'd got himself on the right path at last.

Germany scored twice more before the end, to secure

a thumping 8-0 win, and Serge felt on top of the world as he walked down the tunnel.

"We could do with you at Bayern Munich, you know," Joshua said, next to him.

"I don't think I'd get in over Robben and Ribéry," Serge smiled back, still reeling with his success.

"Maybe not yet, but they're getting on a bit," Kimmich continued, "I think you'd walk into the side."

Serge chuckled. He was experienced enough by now to know that it was never that simple.

18
COOKING UP A STORM

February 2017, Volkswagen Arena, Wolfsberg
Werder Bremen v Wolfsberg

Serge had been watching a game of basketball with his team-mates when he'd first seen it.

Houston Rockets's star player James Harden had nailed a last-minute effort, and the camera had panned back, showing him in celebration – holding an imaginary bowl in one had, a spoon in the other, and stirring the air.

Now, as Serge chested the ball down and thumped it into the roof of the net, he did exactly the same thing in celebration. After all, just like James Harden, Serge was stirring things up.

Since his international debut Serge had really come on a storm at Werder Bremen. This goal was his second in this match, against Wolfsberg, and his tenth so far this season. He was now one of the first names on the team sheet week after week, the big name at the club who the fans were paying to see.

None of that made the feeling of seeing fans on their feet any less special for him, and he ran towards them to be closer to them as they celebrated, still whipping up the air in his make-believe bowl.

At last he was doing the things he'd always wanted to do – playing well and helping his club achieve what they had aimed for. Werder Bremen were now marching up the league, closing in on the European spots they'd been dreaming of.

"Enjoy him now, lads," Max Kruse announced to the rest of the team, as they ran over to join his celebrations. "I don't think he's going to be with us very long."

19
ICE-COLD IN THE BOX

February 2018, Hoffenheim training ground, Hoffenheim

Max Kruse was right.

Serge's contract had a clause that only let him leave Werder Bremen for a minimum fee of eight million euros. Come the summer, Carlo Ancelotti's Bayern Munich decided that eight million euros was a bargain for one of the hottest young prospects in Europe, and so they'd made the offer for Serge.

"We think you need more first-team experience," the Bayern manager had told Serge over the phone, as soon as the deal had been confirmed, "and to be perfectly honest, you won't get that here, so we're going to loan you out to Hoffenheim."

This was exactly the kind of conversation that Serge had had once before, when he was at Arsenal and Arsène had told him how much faith he had in him, but then had loaned him out to West Brom.

But this time Serge didn't hesitate.

He no longer had a problem with taking the longer route to where he wanted to be. He'd also come on in leaps and bounds this season, and he was confident that he could go to Hoffenheim and grow even more as a player.

"That sounds great," he told Carlo.

And now, at the close of another training session, Serge was standing with his latest team, dripping with sweat despite the cold January day, one step closer to playing for one of the biggest clubs on the planet.

As he headed for the showers, the young Hoffenheim manager Julian Nagelsmann beckoned him over.

"Serge, I was hoping we could have a quick chat."

Serge nodded eagerly. This up-and-coming manager, only 30 years old, had been one of the reasons he'd been excited by Bayern's choice of club for him.

"First, I just wanted to let you know that we're all really impressed by the way you've come back from your injuries."

Serge smiled. Two injuries had ruled him out of a number of games at the start of the season, and although they'd been nothing compared to his one at Arsenal, it was still good that his hard work was being noticed.

"I also wanted to talk to you about your role in the team," Julian said. "I watched you at Werder last year and I love your directness. You take players on, you shoot early, it's brilliant – but I need you to be more clinical. You do take a lot of shots from long distance … "

Serge thought of his 45-metre goal that the internet had labelled a 'wonder goal'. He'd picked up the ball in midfield and had looked up to see two midfielders in front of him – and the keeper off his line. Taking a chance, he'd lofted the ball over all three of them, and then watched it bounce into the back of the net.

"… but sometimes I wonder if you waited a little bit, waited until you got into the box, maybe you could get more goals." Julian looked at Serge, hoping he understood what he was saying.

Serge nodded. He always liked taking his shots early, catching everyone off guard, but he was here to grow as a player – and to learn.

He recalled Neymar's performance at the final of the Olympics.

Serge wanted to be as lethal as Neymar had been on that day, the kind of player that would deliver not 10 but 20 or more goals a season.

That was what Bayern Munich wanted from him, and he wanted to deliver it for them.

"More goals is fine by me, boss."

"Excellent. Tomorrow in training we'll start to work on getting you to be ice-cold in the box. Because right now, you're caught between creating chances and finishing them off. Let's turn you into the clinical attacker every club wants."

Julian smiled, patted Serge on the shoulder, then walked back to his office.

20
BACK TO BAYERN

July 2018, Bayern Munich training ground, Munich

Serge stood and looked around Bayern Munich's training ground, a little in awe of his surroundings.

At Hoffenheim he'd been part of a stronger side than when he'd been at Bremen, but he'd played fewer games than he had at Bremen. Nevertheless, with Julian's advice, he'd finished his season at Hoffenheim with another 10 goals and 11 assists, landing the club a third–place finish in the Bundesliga.

And that had meant he'd found his way back here, to Bayern Munich, the club that had offered him a place at the age of 10 – a place that back then his dad had refused, much to Serge's annoyance.

"Anyone would think you're stalking me," Joshua said as he came over to pull Serge into the Bayern training session.

Serge just laughed. He'd been enjoying watching the superstars on the pitch, remembering how he'd done a similar thing on his first day at Arsenal.

The difference was that now he was a budding superstar too, and whenever he got involved with the best club players he could hold his own.

Serge's first appearance for Bayern had to be delayed when one of his injuries from the previous season started playing up again in training.

So he found himself watching Bayern's first game of the season, against manager Niko Kovač's old club Eintracht Frankfurt in the German Super Cup, from the stands. He was joined by Renato Sanches, who'd also returned from a loan spell.

"Watch Lewandowksi, man," Renato said, pointing

out Bayern's illustrious number nine. "You'll have a field day crossing in for him. He turns virtually every chance into a goal."

"Yeah, I know. I've been watching Bayern for years," Serge replied. "I can't wait to play with him."

That day Bayern thrashed Eintracht Frankfurt 5-0 and Lewandowksi scored a hat-trick, but Serge was more interested in the performance of Kingsley Coman, who'd had a very impressive game.

Kingsley played on the wing too, and Serge could now see the quality required to get a place in the Bayern starting eleven.

Over the next few weeks, most of Serge's appearances came from the bench and he was still waiting to get his first goal for the club, to really mark his arrival.

Nevertheless he kept up his fitness and his focus, eager to take any opportunity as soon as it came his way.

The next match was against Freiburg, a game that Bayern needed to win to keep up their title charge. Serge was delighted to see he was in the starting eleven and, as the players prepared to line up in the tunnel, manager Niko Kovač pulled him aside.

"I know you're struggling a bit, and you're finding it harder than at Hoffenheim," Niko began, "but it's supposed to be harder here – we're Bayern Munich. I know you'll deliver for this team," he concluded.

Serge nodded. It was the show of faith he needed.

He marched on to the pitch and threw himself into the game alongside his team-mates.

Bayern were struggling to break down Freiburg, when Serge suddenly picked the ball up on the right-hand side.

Possessed by the desire to deliver for his new manager, his new team-mates and his new fans, he drove into the box, using his pace and strength to brush off the defenders.

His shot was powerful and it flew past the keeper at the near post and nestled in the back of the net.

As the stadium erupted, Serge wheeled away towards the corner flag, trying to process the fact that he was now a Bayern Munich goalscorer! But the deafening noise from the fans meant that he could barely hear himself think.

So, as his team-mates huddled around him, he just focused on the two things that were clear to him at this incredible moment.

One: right now, he was exactly where he needed to be.

And two: he was going to make sure that goal was the first of many.

21
SEEING DOUBLE

May 2019, Allianz Arena, Munich
Bayern Munich v Eintracht Frankfurt

Serge had been dreaming of his first major trophy since he was a little boy, and now one was finally within his grasp.

It was the last day of the Bundesliga season and the title was still in the balance. Borussia Dortmund had pushed Bayern all the way, but it wasn't over yet.

Everything came down to this final game. If Bayern

could get a draw against Eintracht Frankfurt today it would be enough to secure the title.

As Serge sat in the dressing room before the game, he reflected on the progress he'd made. Together with Lewandowski and Coman he was now a key player in Bayern's prolific front three, a trio that had powered the club to the top of the table.

"We've done the hard part," Niko suddenly roared from the middle of the room. "We've got to the last game of the season – and it's all in our hands. This is *our* title and we're not losing it now!"

Inspired, the players headed for the tunnel.

"What should I add if you score today?" David Alaba asked Serge with a grin. After Serge's goal against Dortmund, David had added to Serge's famous celebration, first pretending to taste the air Serge was cooking, and then to add pepper to it.

"Let's just try to win the game," Serge said, shaking his head. It said a lot about how many trophies Bayern had won that David could be joking around before a match like this.

Bayern were the favourites, but Eintracht Frankfurt

were a strong team and were more than capable of causing the home team problems.

Bayern made the perfect start, and after just four minutes Kingsley Coman slotted home the opener.

Serge was desperate to get on the scoresheet as well, and he thought he'd done so about 20 minutes later. But after a long VAR review the goal was disallowed for offside.

At half-time, Bayern still led 1-0 and there was a party atmosphere in the dressing room. Needing only a draw, they were confident the title was coming home.

"When are you bringing on Franck and Arjen?" Mats Hummels shouted across to their manager. Everybody knew that Franck Ribéry and Arjen Robben were leaving the club at the end of this season, so giving them some time in this game would be an appropriate gesture.

"Let's not get carried away, lads," Kovač warned. "We're only one goal ahead. We need that second one to kill the game off. So come on, go out and get it!"

He was right to be concerned. Not long into the second half, Sébastian Haller poked Frankfurt back on level terms.

Immediately, Serge felt the attitude of the Bayern players change. They became more focused, more deliberate in their movements, and their pace and work rate increased. This team was *not* going to have the title snatched from them in the last moments of the season.

Three minutes after Frankfurt's equaliser David Alaba put Bayern back ahead.

Five minutes later Renato Sanches gave Bayern a 3-1 lead.

With the game now won Kovač began to make the changes that the Bayern fans had been begging for. First, Ribéry replaced Kingsley Coman. Then, a few moments later, Serge saw his number go up. He was coming off for Arjen Robben.

He high-fived Robben and gave him a hug.

"I'm passing the torch to you now," Robben joked. "It's up to you to make sure that Bayern keep winning trophies."

In a perfect twist, both Robben and Ribery scored, confirming an emphatic 5-1 win for Bayern.

Serge half-expected this team of serial winners to be unfazed at winning yet another title, but the look on all his team-mates' faces revealed just how much this meant. He could feel the joy amongst them as they celebrated with the beautiful trophy.

Serge was still feeling euphoric when his turn to hold the trophy eventually came, and he kept looking at it in his hands, unable to believe it was actually there.

After all, there had been so many times in his career he'd thought this incredible moment was going to be impossible.

Then it struck him – he would actually have the chance to lift his second professional trophy very soon, because Bayern still had a cup final to play. They could still do the double.

A week later Serge found himself in Berlin, facing Leipzig in the cup final.

There seemed to be as many Bayern fans in the Berlin stadium as Serge was used to seeing in their home games, and he was overwhelmed by the atmosphere. This, he thought, was what top-level football was all about.

Serge set about being a constant thorn in Leipzig's side throughout the match and the Leipzig players struggled with his pace and quick feet.

He was disappointed to come off with 20 minutes of the match left, but he knew he'd played his part. He also knew why he *had* to come off.

"Let the old boys finish this off now," Kovač said, as he sent on Arjen Robben and Franck Ribéry for their final appearances in a Bayern shirt.

Serge couldn't deny either of these two great players one last appearance for their club.

He watched from the bench as Bayern ran out comfortable 3-0 winners.

And then, for the second time in seven days, he celebrated with his team as Manuel Neuer held a trophy above his head.

Standing on the podium, being showered in confetti, Serge recalled his crushing disappointment when Arsenal had twice won the FA Cup without him.

Now he'd done the double in his first season with Bayern Munich – and he was already hungry to add to his trophy collection.

22

SERGE'S MARATHON

November 2019, Commerzbank Arena, Frankfurt
Euro 2020 Qualifier, Germany v Northern Ireland

With Timo Werner and Joshua Kimmich sitting either side of him in the dressing room, Serge just had to smile.

Many times as young boys they'd sat in front of the TV, watching Germany playing in international tournaments, and now all three of them were representing their country – part of the Germany squad for the qualifying stages of the 2020 Euros.

They were playing in this final qualifier against Northern Ireland – and it started badly, with Michael Smith giving their opponents a shock lead.

But Serge was unfazed. He knew better than anyone that if things didn't go according to plan, well – you could always get them back on track.

Leading by example, he started to take control of the match, firing in an equaliser on the half-volley just 10 minutes after Northern Ireland's opener.

"Didn't I teach you that when we were, like, thirteen?" Joshua bellowed in his ear.

Leon Goretzka was next to get his name on the scoresheet, then Serge scored his second goal of the game, smashing a shot across the keeper only a few minutes into the second half. Now 3-1 up, Germany were firmly in control.

With half an hour left, Julian Brandt played a ball into the middle of the pitch.

Serge ran on to it and his first touch took him away from goal and into the box. A defender tried to force him off the pitch, but Serge held on, keeping control of the ball.

As the keeper came rushing out, Serge neatly poked it around him.

GOAL!

"That's your second hat-trick for Germany! That's mad!" Julian Brandt shouted in his direction, as Serge simply punched the air. He wanted to look as cool and collected as he had the first time, back in San Marino.

Germany got two more goals before the end of the match, sealing a thumping 6-1 win.

They had not just qualified for the Euros – they'd qualified at the top of their group – and they'd done it in style. They couldn't have sent a clearer message to world football.

At the whistle Serge looked around, suddenly feeling in awe of his surroundings.

He was now in contention for his first international trophy with Germany, not to mention his first Champions League trophy with Bayern Munich, thanks to his four goals against Tottenham last month.

Serge smiled as he remembered how, as a boy, he'd been so convinced that his career would be a simple route to the top – scouted for an academy, signed up by a big club, then whisked into their first team, where he'd start winning everything there was to win.

The path that had got him to this point in his career hadn't been the straight road he'd expected at all. As his dad had said, it had been a marathon, not a sprint.

But as he stood here now, he wouldn't change that for the world.

Every tough experience, every knockback he'd suffered, had made him who he was – Serge Gnabry, Bayern Munich's deadliest weapon and Germany's brightest light.

And his marathon run to the very top of football wasn't over yet.

HOW MANY
HAVE YOU READ?

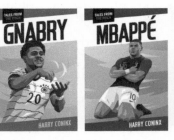

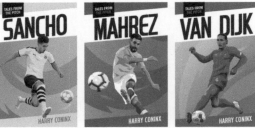